BOOGIE, ROCK & COUNTRY

LEVEL 3

BY JAMES BASTIEN

kjos NEIL A. KJOS MUSIC COMPANY • SAN DIEGO, CALIFORNIA

Preface

Boogie, Rock & Country contains a variety of popular styles arranged in a progressive order of difficulty. This book may be used to supplement **Bastien Piano Basics**, or any piano method at a similar level.

We offer you our best wishes for an enjoyable time with **Boogie, Rock & Country**!

Neil A. Kjos Music Company
James Bastien
Jane Smisor Bastien

About the composer

James Bastien has written a great deal of music that has been enjoyed by both children and adults.

He has been a faculty member at Notre Dame, Tulane, and Loyola Universities, and a summer faculty member at Tanglewood and the National Music Camp at Interlochen, Michigan. When he was a student at Southern Methodist University, his piano teacher was Gyorgy Sandor.

Mr. Bastien now resides in La Jolla, California, where he and his wife continue to write music of interest to piano students.

Contents

✔ *

*To reinforce the feeling of achievement, the teacher or student may put a ✔ when the page has been mastered.

ISBN 0-8497-9337-8

4

Cucaracha Boogie

Lively

The Spanish word *cucaracha* means cockroach.

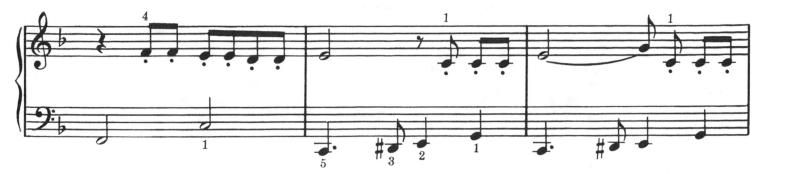

6

Wagon Train

Moderato

*The eighth notes may be played in a long-short rhythm to give a Western effect. One way to practice this is to say:

doo bah doo bah doo bah doo bah

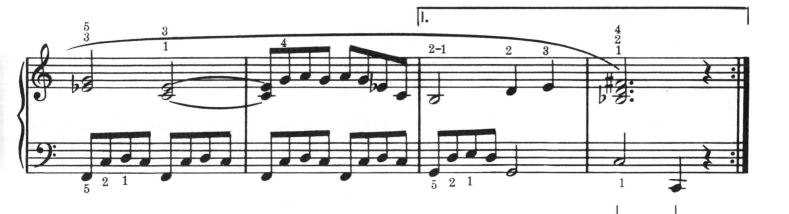

Indian War Dance Rock

Bright rock beat

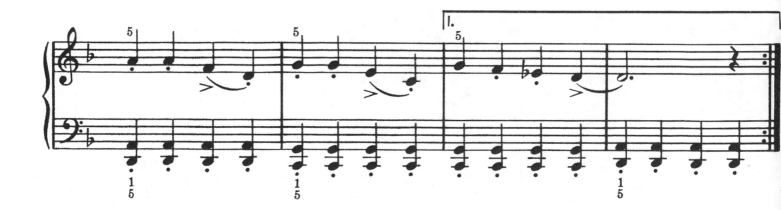

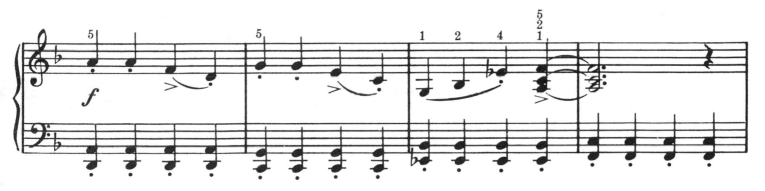

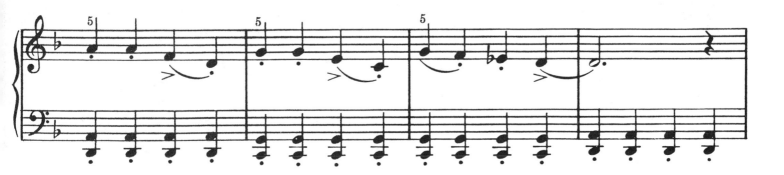

Cheerleader Boogie

Moderate boogie beat

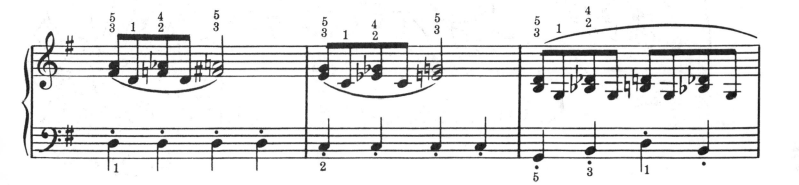

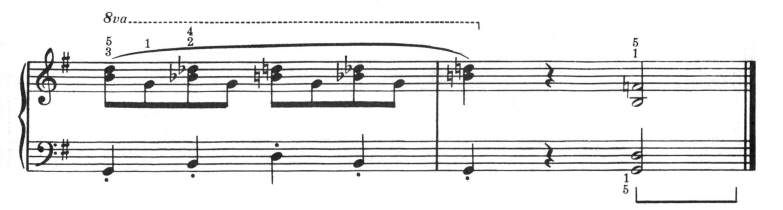

Fast Fingers Rag

Moderato

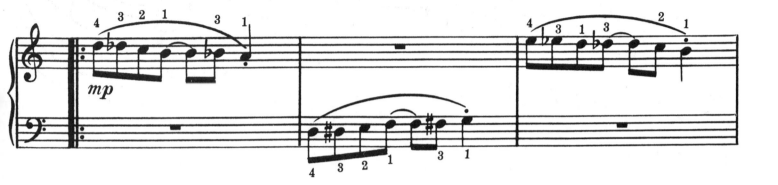

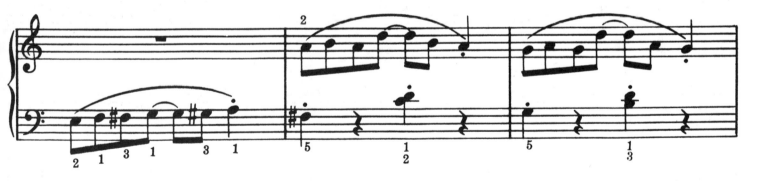

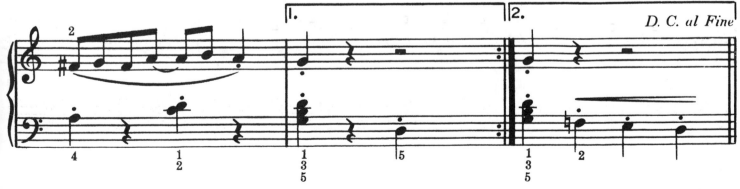

American Patrol Boogie

Bright march beat

F.W. Meacham

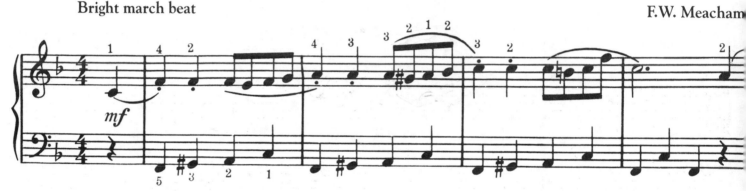

WP240

to next strain

Fine

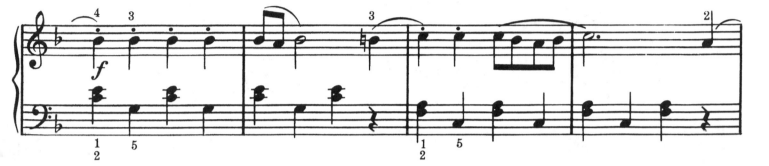

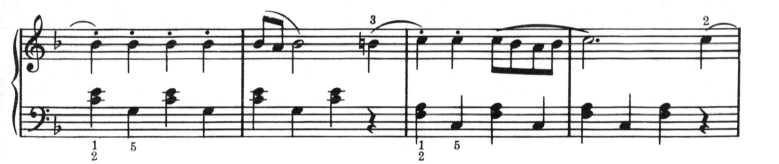

D. C. al Fine

WP240

Chopsticks

Allegro

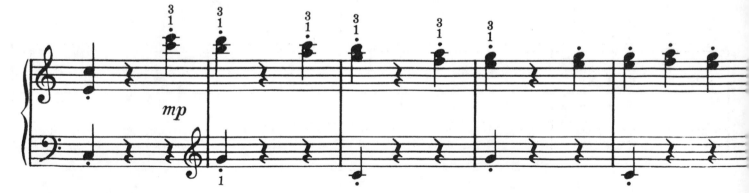

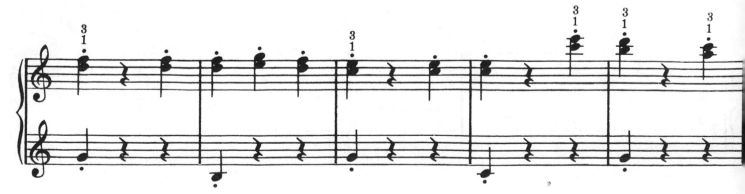

Maple Leaf Rag

Moderato

Scott Joplin

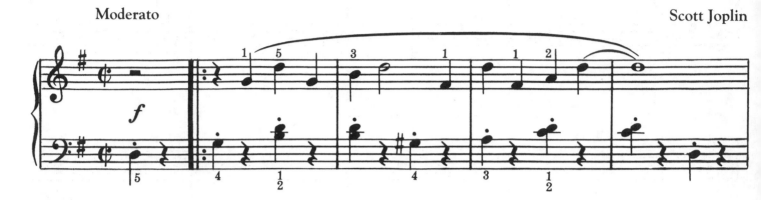

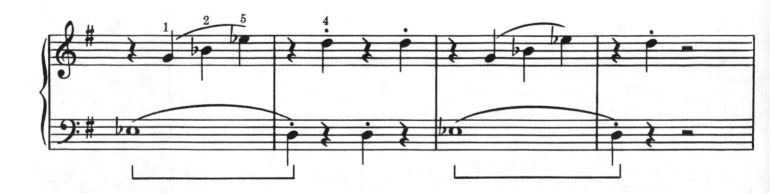

WP240

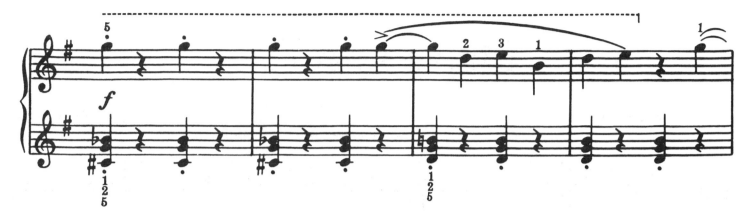

Cryin' Over You

Moderato

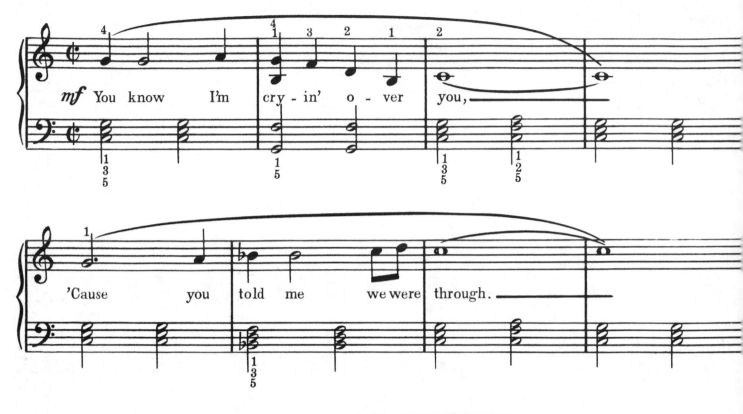

You know I'm cry - in' o - ver you,

'Cause you told me we were through. _____

I felt that cer - tain feel - ing right from the start,

I thought that we would nev - er part!

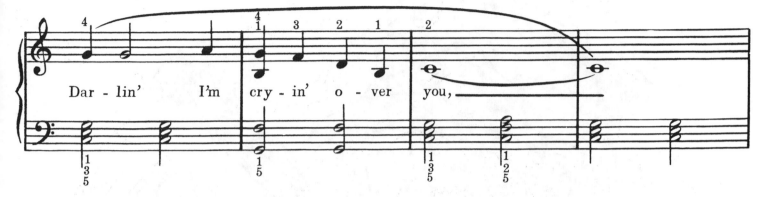

Dar - lin' I'm cry - in' o - ver you,

I think you feel that way too.

I miss you more than I can real - ly say,

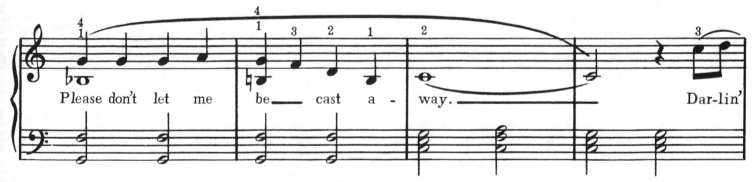

Please don't let me be cast a - way. Dar-lin'

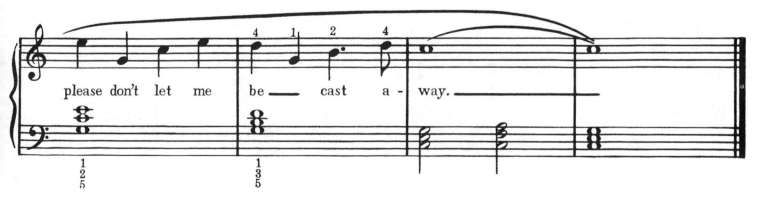

please don't let me be cast a - way.

New Orleans Blues

Moderato

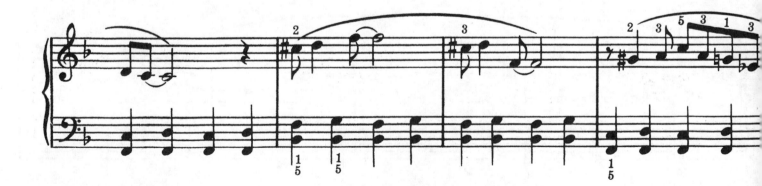

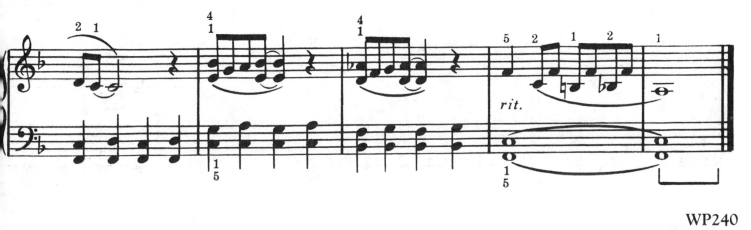

Choo-Choo Boogie

Lively

WP240